Garfield
in Disguise

JIM DAVIS

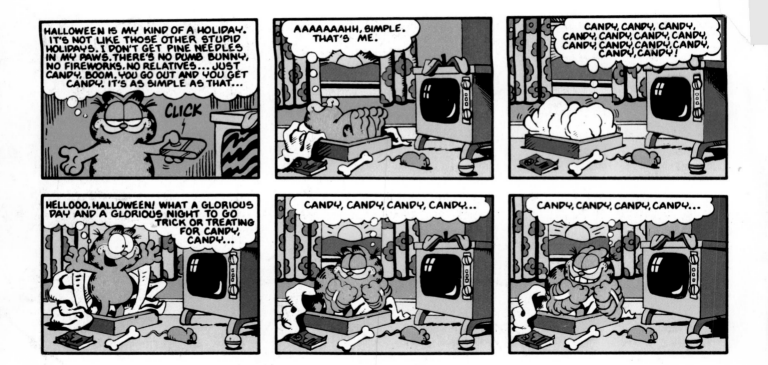

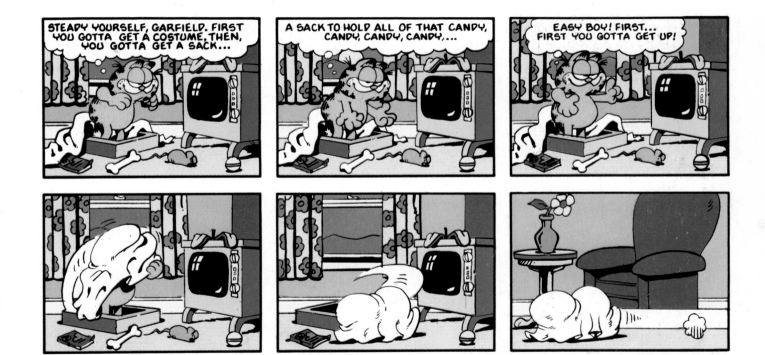

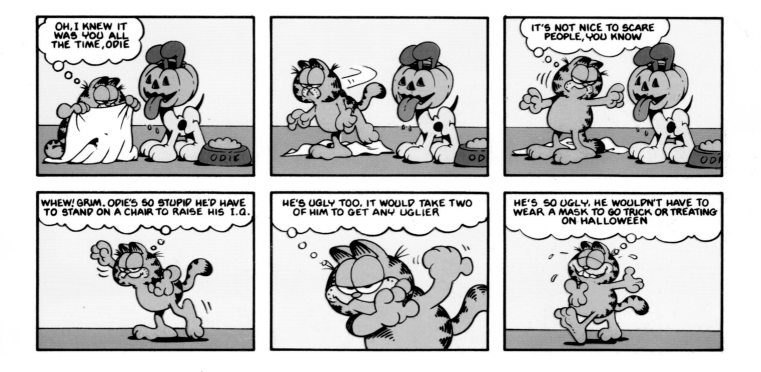

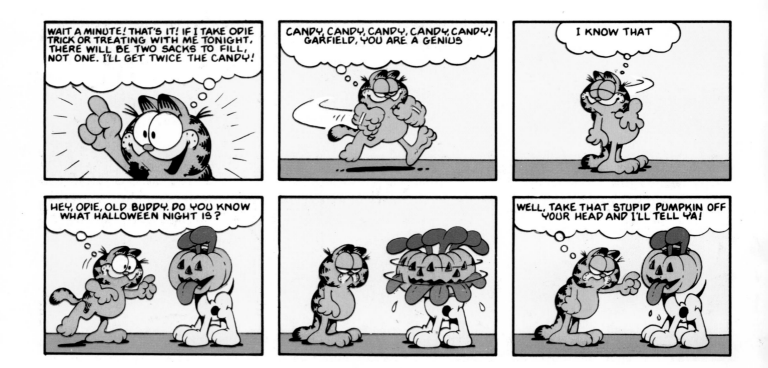

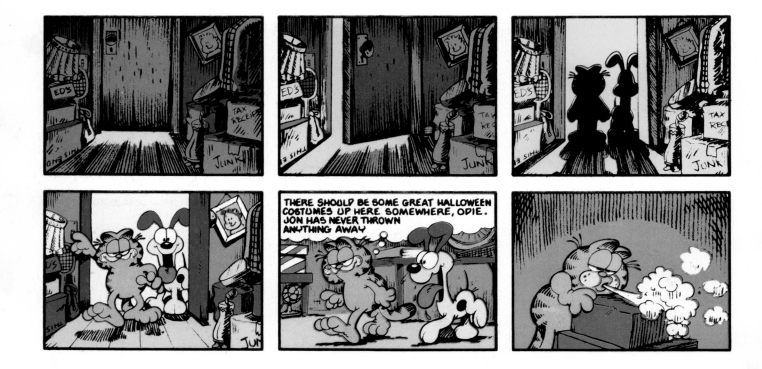

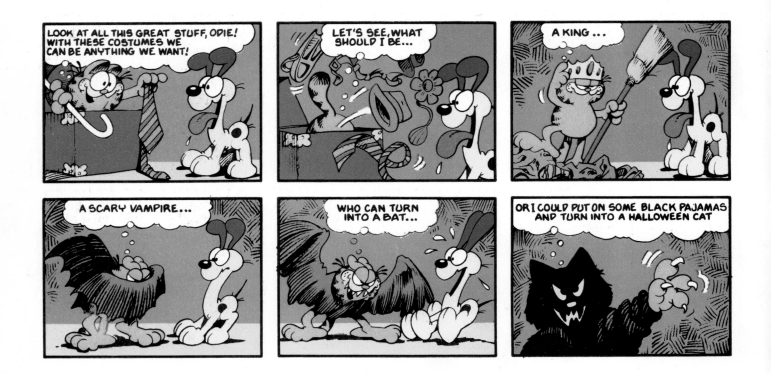

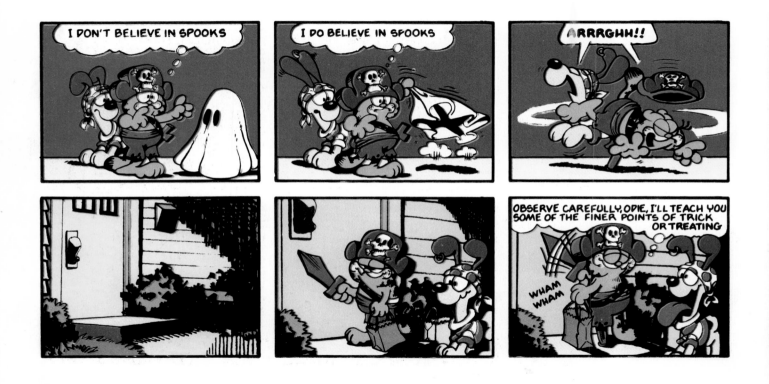

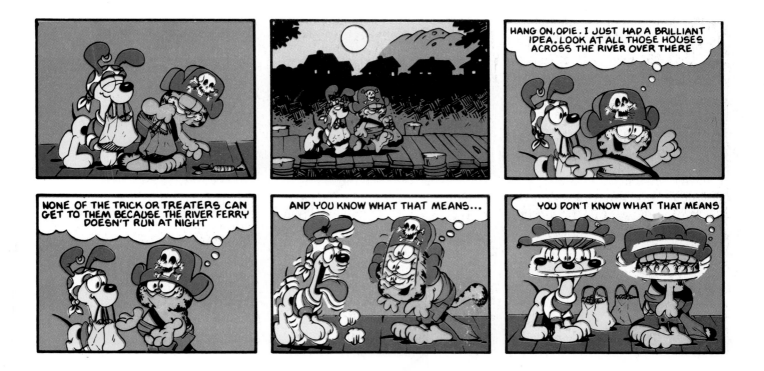

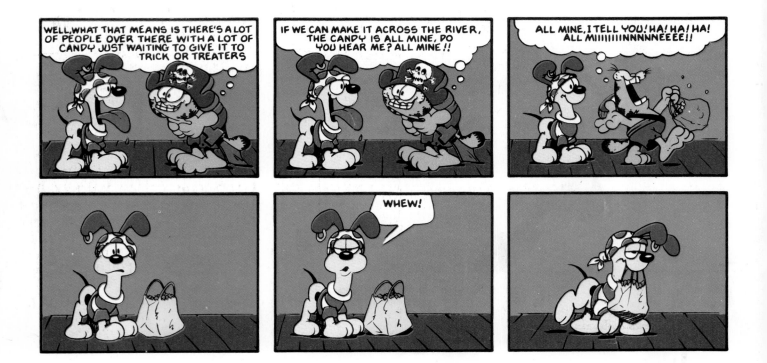

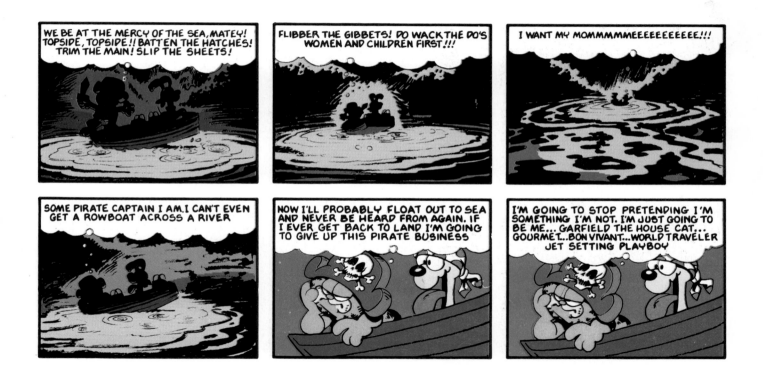

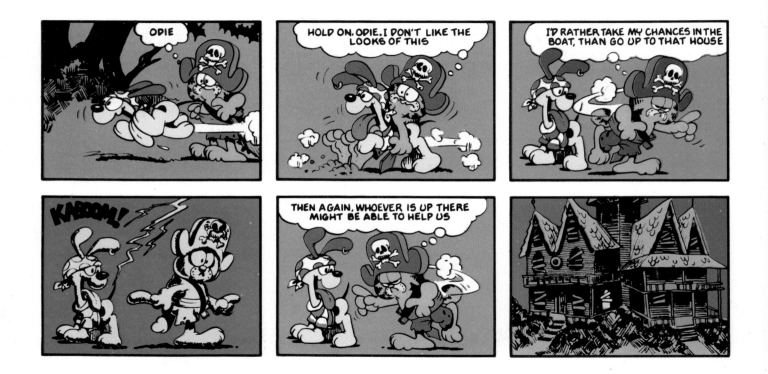

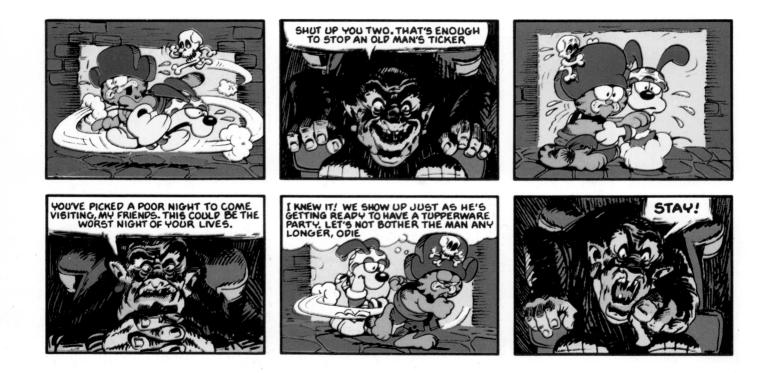

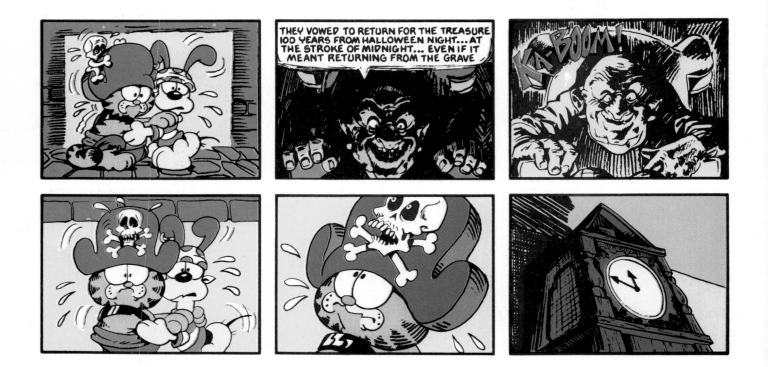

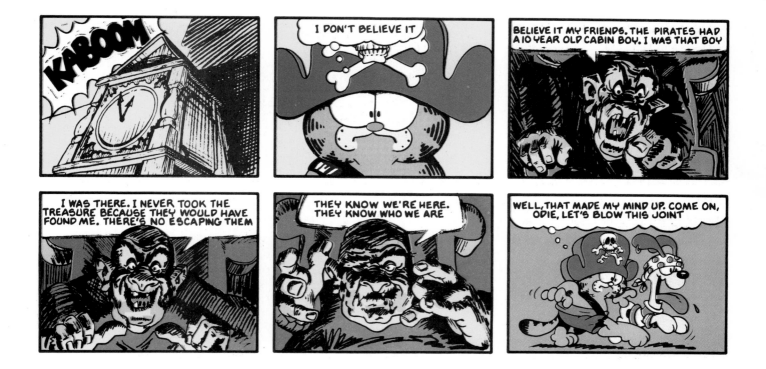

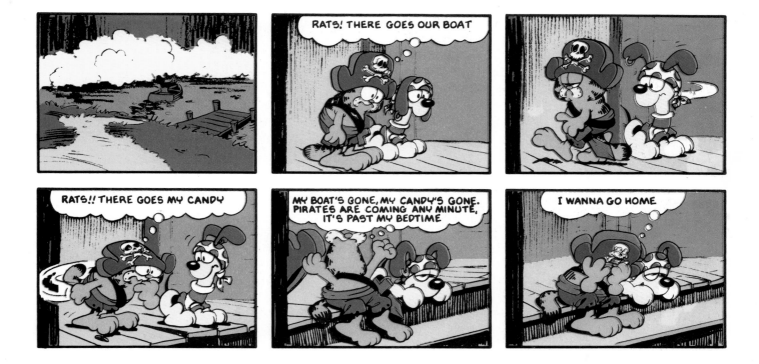

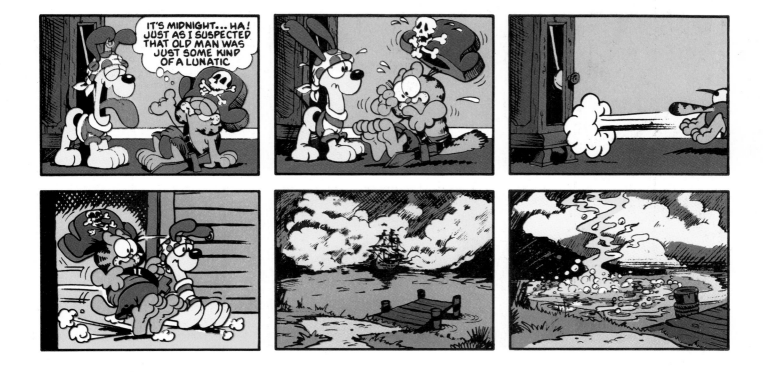

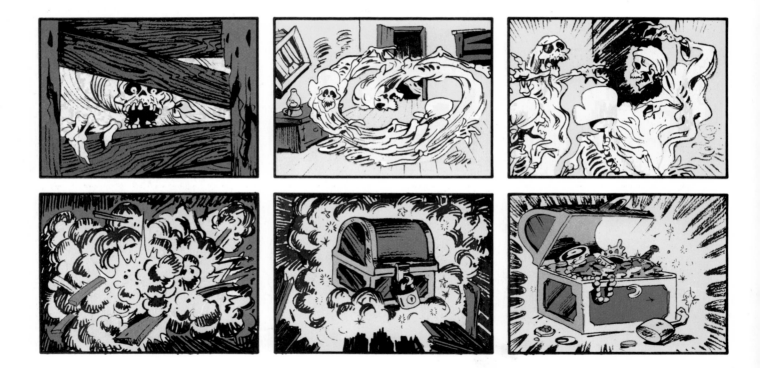

WHY US?! WHY DON'T THEY LEAVE US ALONE?

THEY GOT THEIR STUPID TREASURE. I CAN'T FIGURE IT OUT. WHAT IS IT ODIE?

THE RING! OF COURSE! THEY CAME FOR THE RING!

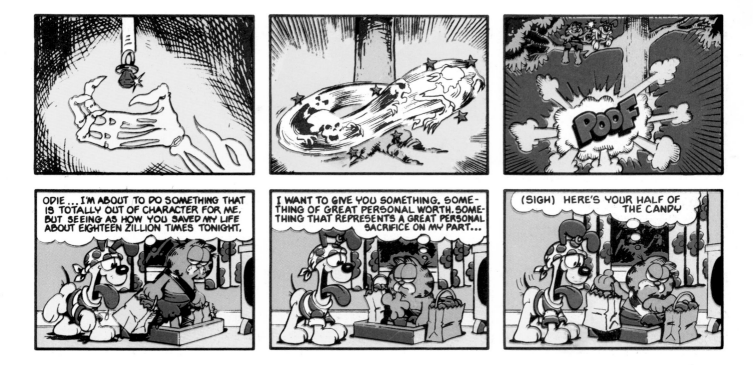

Garfield's Thanksgiving

JIM DAVIS

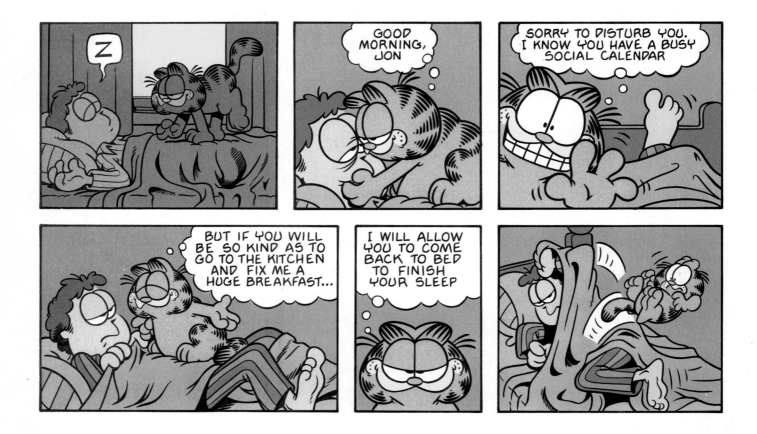

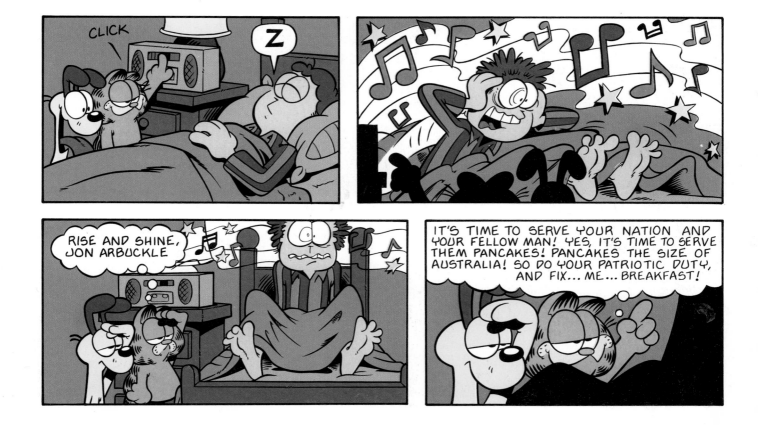

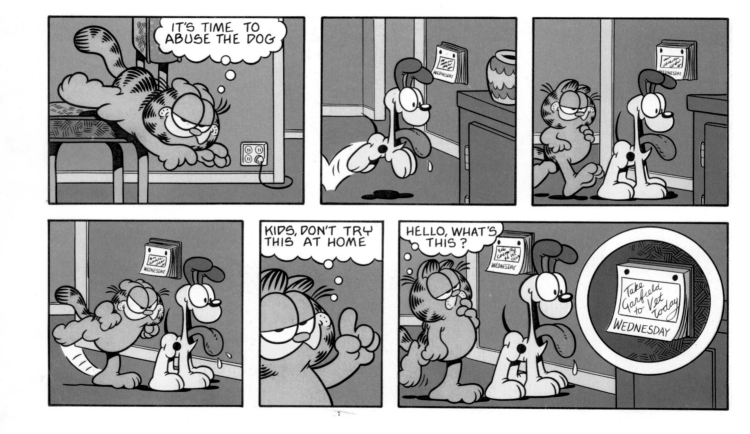

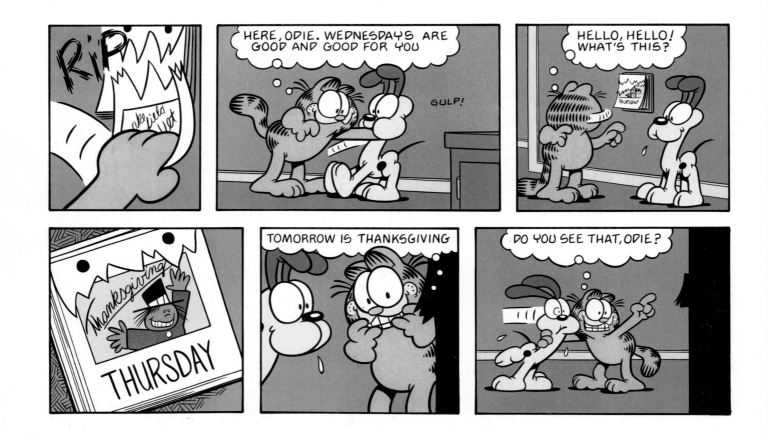

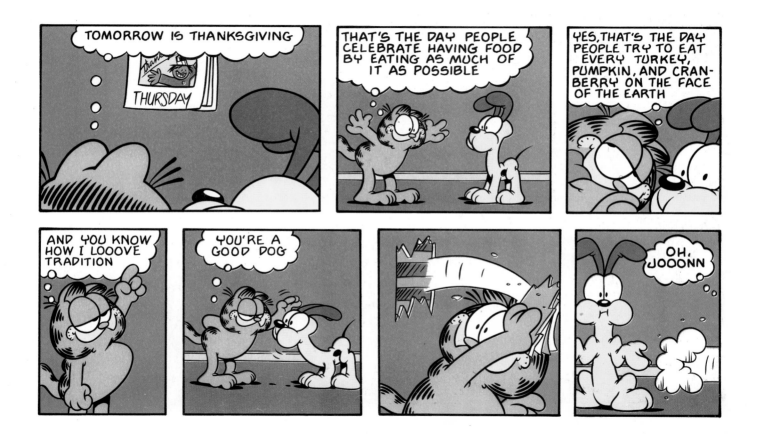

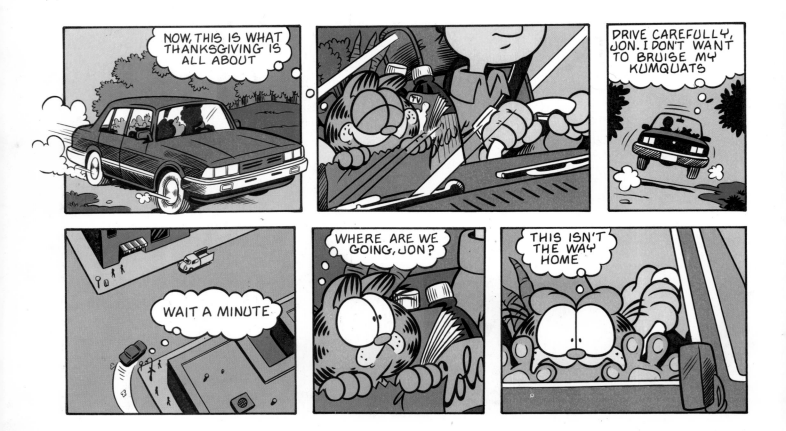

SHOO-BOP-DOO-WOP. GOT A DATE WITH MY DREAM CHICK. GONNA IMPRESS HER AND MAKE HER MY GIRL

OH, WOE IS ME. I'M BEING PUT ON A DIET AND I'M GOING TO DIE

HERE, GARFIELD. HAVE SOME FOOD

ACCORDING TO YOUR DIET, YOU GET THIS

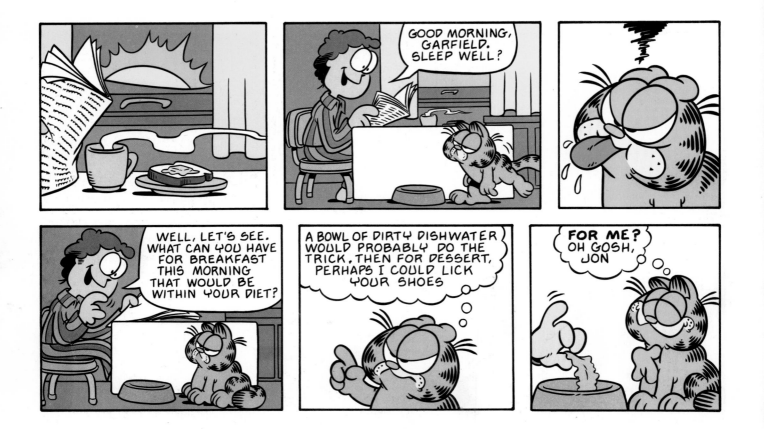

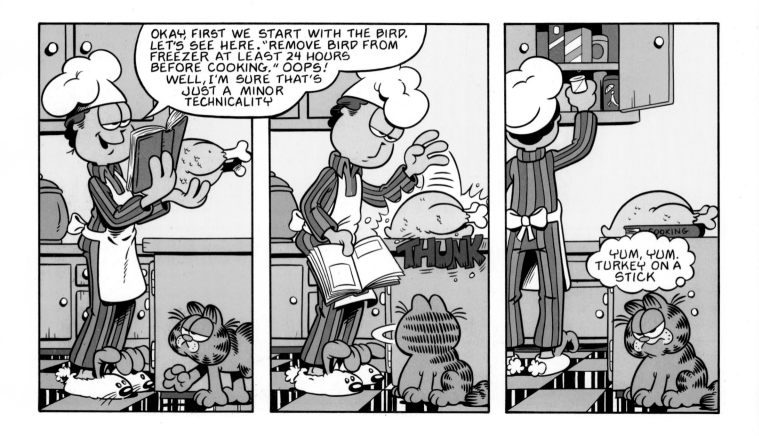

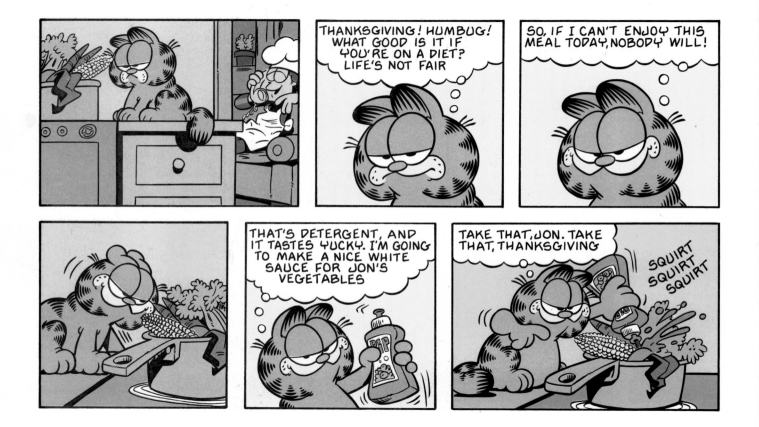

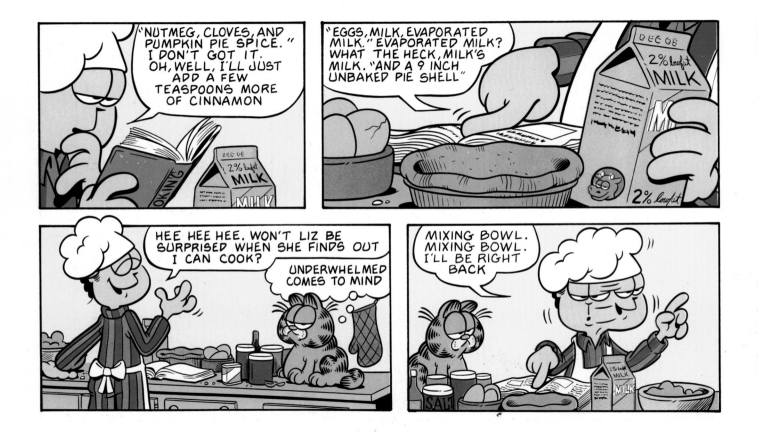

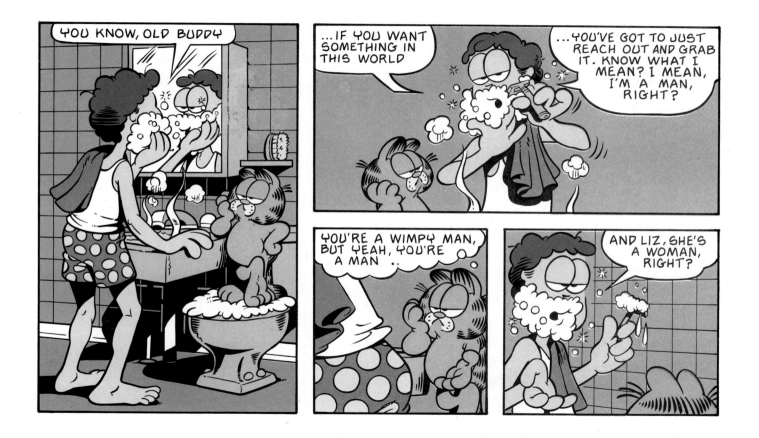

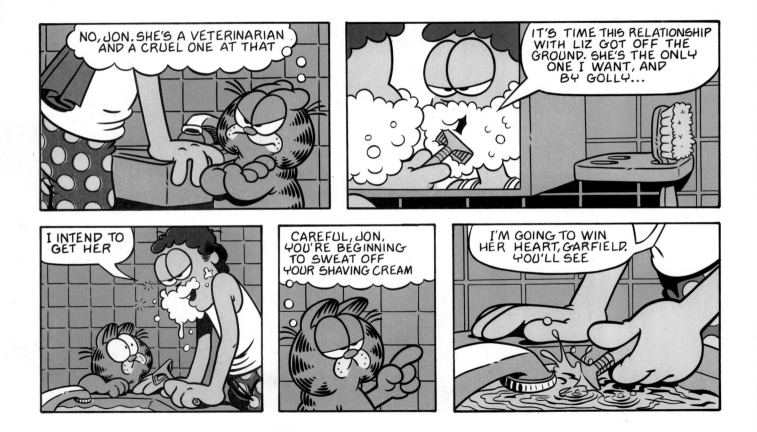

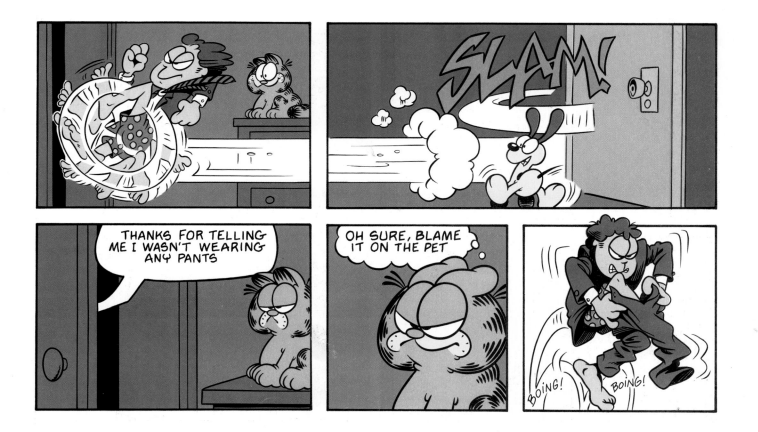

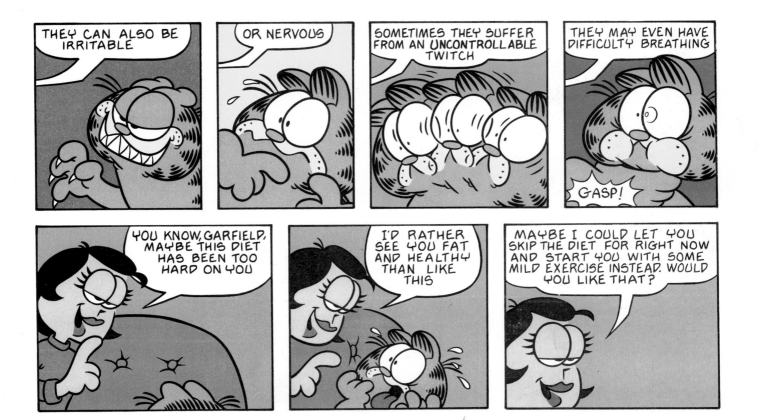

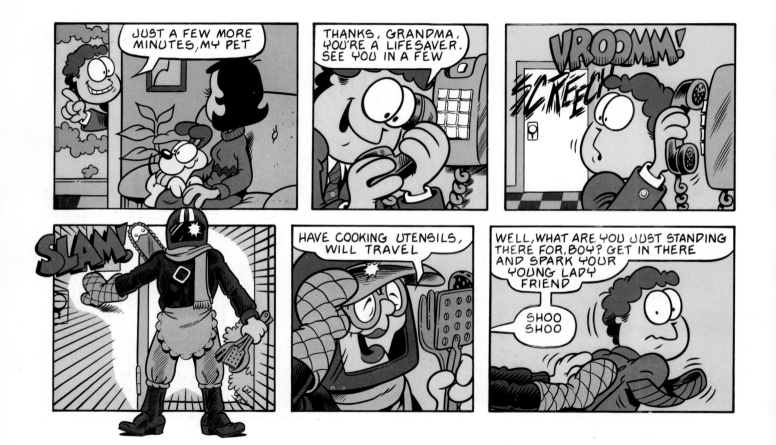

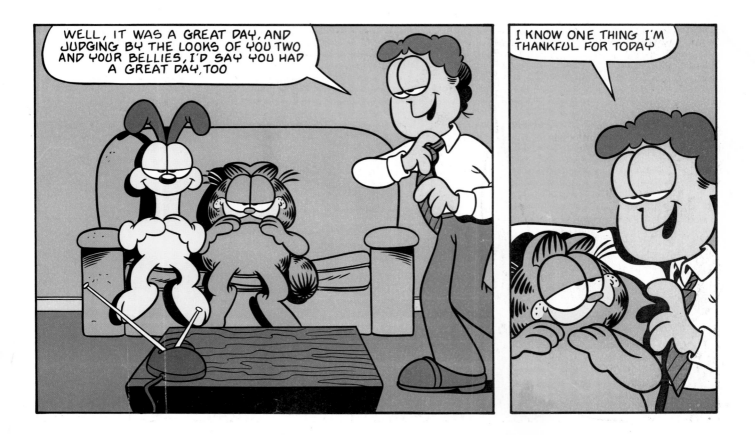

A
Garfield
Christmas

JIM DAVIS

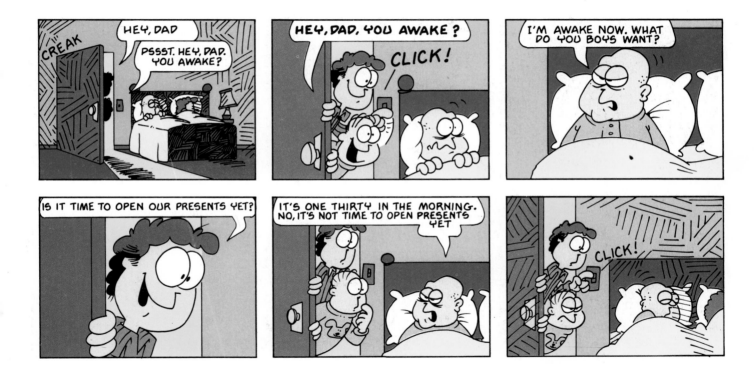

WHAT HAPPENED? DID YOU BOYS OVERSLEEP OR SOMETHING?

SOMEONE TURNED OUR ALARM CLOCK OFF

I KNOW

WELL, WHAT DO YOU BOYS WANT TO DO FIRST? DO YOU WANT TO DO CHORES, DO YOU WANT TO EAT BREAKFAST, OR DO YOU WANT TO OPEN PRESENTS?

PRESENTS!

STRIPS, SPECIALS, OR BESTSELLING BOOKS . . .
GARFIELD'S ON EVERYONE'S MENU
Don't miss even one episode in the Tubby Tabby's hilarious series!

__GARFIELD AT LARGE (#1) 32013/$6.95
__GARFIELD GAINS WEIGHT (#2) 32008/$6.95
__GARFIELD BIGGER THAN LIFE (#3) 32007/$6.95
__GARFIELD WEIGHS IN (#4) 32010/$6.95
__GARFIELD TAKES THE CAKE (#5) 32009/$6.95
__GARFIELD EATS HIS HEART OUT (#6) 32018/$6.95
__GARFIELD SITS AROUND THE HOUSE (#7) 32011/$6.95
__GARFIELD TIPS THE SCALES (#8) 33580/$6.95
__GARFIELD LOSES HIS FEET (#9) 31805/$6.95
__GARFIELD MAKES IT BIG (#10) 31928/$6.95
__GARFIELD ROLLS ON (#11) 32634/$6.95
__GARFIELD OUT TO LUNCH (#12) 33118/$6.95
__GARFIELD FOOD FOR THOUGHT (#13) 34129/$6.95
__GARFIELD SWALLOWS HIS PRIDE (#14) 34725/$6.95
__GARFIELD WORLDWIDE (#15) 35158/$6.95
__GARFIELD ROUNDS OUT (#16) 35388/$6.95
__GARFIELD CHEWS THE FAT (#17) 35956/$6.95
__GARFIELD GOES TO WAIST (#18) 36430/$6.95
__GARFIELD HANGS OUT (#19) 36835/$6.95
__GARFIELD TAKES UP SPACE (#20) 37029/$6.95

__GARFIELD SAYS A MOUTHFUL (#21) 37368/$6.95
__GARFIELD BY THE POUND (#22) 37579/$6.95
__GARFIELD KEEPS HIS CHINS UP (#23) 37959/$6.95
__GARFIELD TAKES HIS LICKS (#24) 38170/$6.95
__GARFIELD HITS THE BIG TIME (#25) 38332/$6.95
__GARFIELD PULLS HIS WEIGHT (#26) 38666/$6.95
__GARFIELD DISHES IT OUT (#27) 39287/$6.95
__GARFIELD LIFE IN THE FAT LANE (#28) 39776/$6.95
__GARFIELD TONS OF FUN (#29) 40386/$6.95
__GARFIELD BIGGER AND BETTER (#30) 40770/$6.95
__GARFIELD HAMS IT UP (#31) 41241/$6.95
__GARFIELD THINKS BIG (#32) 41671/$6.95

GARFIELD AT HIS SUNDAY BEST!
__GARFIELD TREASURY 32106/$11.95
__THE SECOND GARFIELD TREASURY 33276/$10.95
__THE THIRD GARFIELD TREASURY 32635/$11.00
__THE FOURTH GARFIELD TREASURY 34726/$10.95
__THE FIFTH GARFIELD TREASURY 36268/$12.00
__THE SIXTH GARFIELD TREASURY 37367/$10.95
__THE SEVENTH GARFIELD TREASURY 38427/$10.95
__THE EIGHTH GARFIELD TREASURY 39778/$12.00
__THE NINTH GARFIELD TREASURY 41670/$12.50

Please send me the BALLANTINE BOOKS I have checked above. I am enclosing $_____. (Please add $2.00 for the first book and $.50 for each additional book for postage and handling and include the appropriate state sales tax.) Send check or money order (no cash or C.O.D.'s) to Ballantine Mail Sales Dept. TA, 400 Hahn Road, Westminster, MD 21157.

To order by phone, call 1-800-733-3000 and use your major credit card.

Prices and numbers are subject to change without notice. Valid in the U.S. only. All orders are subject to availability.

Name_____

Address_____

City_____ State_____ Zip_____

Allow at least 4 weeks for delivery   5/97

BIRTHDAYS, HOLIDAYS, OR ANY DAY . . .

Keep GARFIELD on your calendar all year 'round!

GARFIELD TV SPECIALS
__BABES & BULLETS   36339/$5.95
__GARFIELD GOES HOLLYWOOD   34580/$6.95
__GARFIELD'S HALLOWEEN ADVENTURE   33045/$6.95
  (formerly GARFIELD IN DISGUISE)
__GARFIELD'S FELINE FANTASY   36902/$6.95
__GARFIELD IN PARADISE   33796/$6.95
__GARFIELD IN THE ROUGH   32242/$6.95
__GARFIELD ON THE TOWN   31542/$6.95
__GARFIELD'S THANKSGIVING   35650/$6.95
__HERE COMES GARFIELD   32021/$6.95
__GARFIELD GETS A LIFE   37375/$6.95
__A GARFIELD CHRISTMAS   35368/$5.95

Please send me the BALLANTINE BOOKS I have checked above. I am enclosing $_____. (Please add $2.00 for the first book and $.50 for each additional book for postage and handling and include the appropriate state sales tax.) Send check or money order (no cash or C.O.D.'s) to Ballantine Mail Sales Dept. TA, 400 Hahn Road, Westminster, MD 21157.

To order by phone, call 1-800-733-3000 and use your major credit card.

Prices and numbers are subject to change without notice. Valid in the U.S. only. All orders are subject to availability.

GREETINGS FROM GARFIELD!
GARFIELD POSTCARD BOOKS FOR ALL OCCASIONS.
__GARFIELD THINKING OF YOU   36516/$6.95
__GARFIELD WORDS TO LIVE BY   36679/$6.95
__GARFIELD BIRTHDAY GREETINGS   36771/$7.95
__GARFIELD BE MY VALENTINE   37121/$7.95
__GARFIELD SEASON'S GREETINGS   37435/$8.95
__GARFIELD VACATION GREETINGS   37774/$10.00
__GARFIELD'S THANK YOU POSTCARD BOOK   37893/$10.00

ALSO FROM GARFIELD:
__GARFIELD: HIS NINE LIVES   32061/$9.95
__THE GARFIELD BOOK OF CAT NAMES   35082/$5.95
__THE GARFIELD TRIVIA BOOK   33771/$6.95
__THE UNABRIDGED UNCENSORED
  UNBELIEVABLE GARFIELD   33772/$5.95
__GARFIELD: THE ME BOOK   36545/$7.95
__GARFIELD'S JUDGMENT DAY   36755/$6.95
__THE TRUTH ABOUT CATS   37226/$6.95

Name_____

Address_____

City_____ State_____ Zip_____
30   Allow at least 4 weeks for delivery   7/93 TA-267

Like to get a **COOL CAT**alog stuffed with great **GARFIELD** products? Then just write down the information below, stuff it in an envelope and mail it back to us...or you can fill in the card on our website - HTTP://www.GARFIELD.com. We'll get one out to you in two shakes of a cat's tail!

Name:
Address:
City:
State:
Zip:
Phone:
Date of Birth:
Sex:

Please mail your information to:

Artistic Greetings
Dept. #02-7002
Elmira, NY 14925

© PAWS